Over three hundred cultures tell the story of a great flood in their distant past. Some of these stories have been handed down by word of mouth from generation to generation, while others have been inscribed on clay tablets or carved on hard stone slabs and ancient walls. Fragile parchments painted thousands of years ago depict turbulent waters covering the earth and destroying cities and civilisations. Holy scriptures tell of a man and his family who survive a great deluge in an ark, with two of every animal on board. The stories vary considerably, but they all have a common theme of the earth being cleansed of evil and of the rebirth of goodness.

Some claim to have found evidence of a great flood, while others claim the deluge stories are merely folk law that have spread from one culture to the next. People keep searching for remains of the great ark. They climb to the top of the tallest mountains, scan the earth from satellites, and endlessly debate the evidence. No doubt the speculation will continue for generations to come, more evidence of great floods will be unearthed, and new stories will unfold. This tale could well be one of those stories.

J. W. 2003

Two by Two

JOHN WINCH

A Scholastic Press
book
from
Scholastic Australia

There was a time, long ago, when the animals
lived together in peace and contentment.

Life was good. The days were long and warm, filled only
with the search for food, a companion . . .

and a dry place to sleep.

One day darkness covered the earth.
Wild winds blew.
Lightning flashed and thunder echoed.
It began to rain.

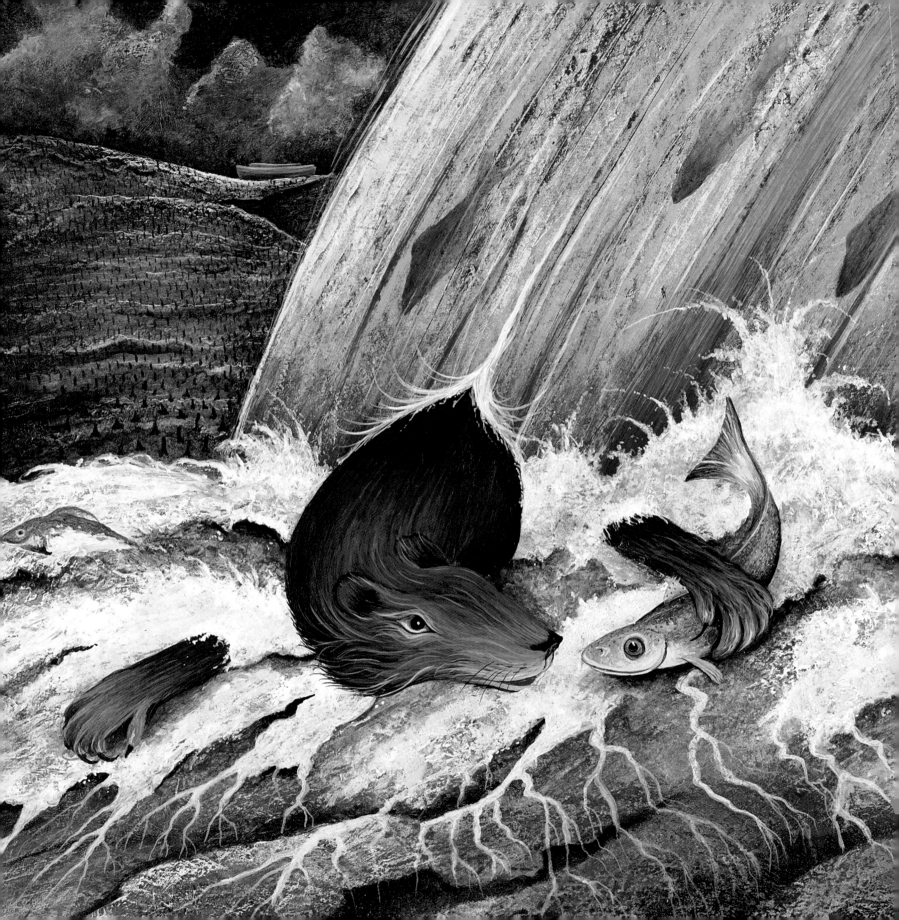

It rained and rained until the rivers rose.

The rivers overflowed and flooded the plains and deserts.

Jungles vanished.

The North and South Poles disappeared.

It rained until the mountain peaks were covered . . .

and every village and city destroyed.

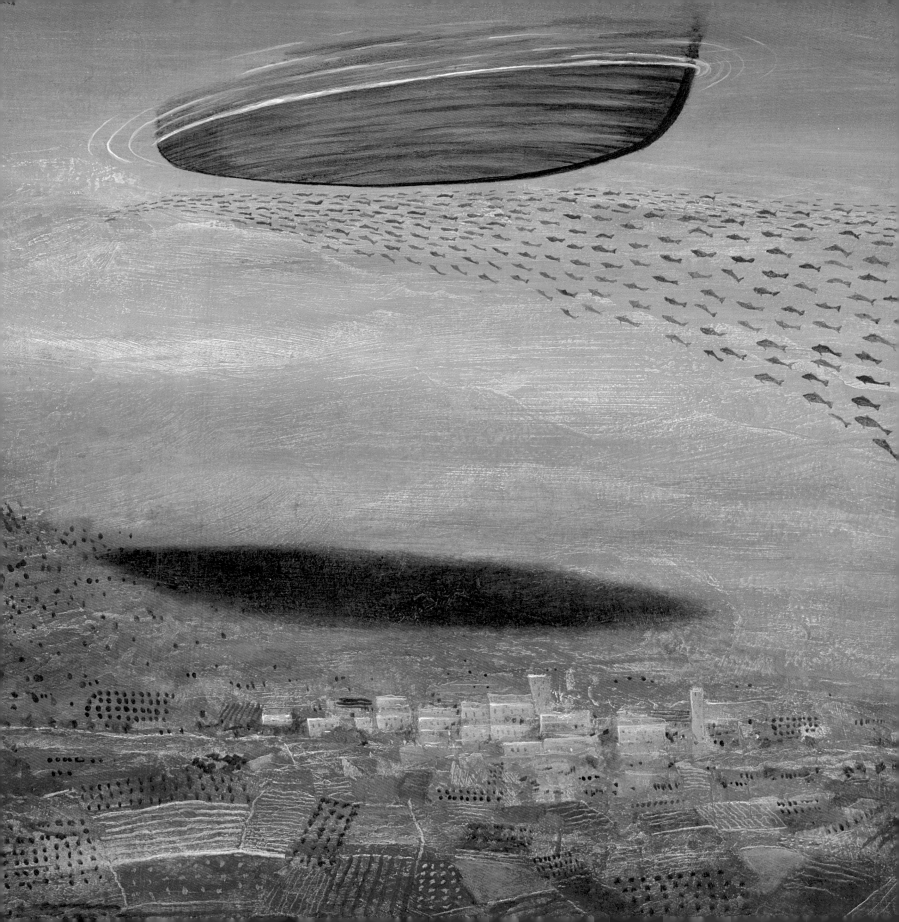

Some proud animals did not seek shelter until the last minute.

For others it was almost too late.

Finally, there was only one warm, dry place left.

When there was no rain left to fall, the sun shone . . .

and life was good again.

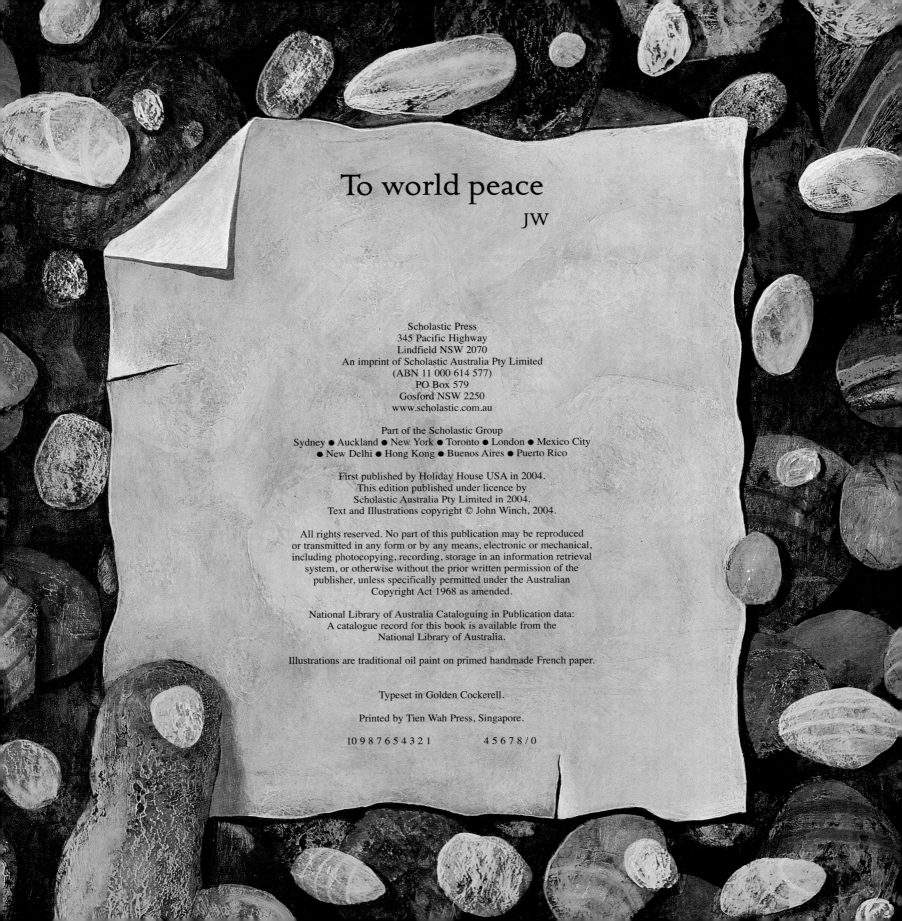

To world peace

JW

Scholastic Press
345 Pacific Highway
Lindfield NSW 2070
An imprint of Scholastic Australia Pty Limited
(ABN 11 000 614 577)
PO Box 579
Gosford NSW 2250
www.scholastic.com.au

Part of the Scholastic Group
Sydney ● Auckland ● New York ● Toronto ● London ● Mexico City
● New Delhi ● Hong Kong ● Buenos Aires ● Puerto Rico

First published by Holiday House USA in 2004.
This edition published under licence by
Scholastic Australia Pty Limited in 2004.
Text and Illustrations copyright © John Winch, 2004.

National Library of Australia Cataloguing in Publication data:
A catalogue record for this book is available from the
National Library of Australia.

Illustrations are traditional oil paint on primed handmade French paper.

Typeset in Golden Cockerell.

Printed by Tien Wah Press, Singapore.

10 9 8 7 6 5 4 3 2 1   4 5 6 7 8 / 0